Malachy Doyle
Illustrated by Christopher Corr

White Wolves series consultant: Sue Ellis,
Centre for Literacy in Primary Education

This book can be used in the White Wolves Guided Reading
programme by readers of average ability in Year 2

First paperback edition 2012
First published in hardback in 2012 by
A & C Black
Bloomsbury Publishing Plc
50 Bedford Square
London
WC1B 3DP

www.acblack.com
www.malachydoyle.com

ISBN 978-1-4081-3950-9

A CIP catalogue for this book is available from the British Library.

This book is produced using paper that is made from wood
grown in managed, sustainable forests. It is natural, renewable
and recyclable. The logging and manufacturing processes conform
to the environmental regulations of the country of origin.

Printed and bound in China by C&C Offset Printing Co.

Chapter One

Prince Rama was a great warrior, and he had a beautiful wife named Sita.

Rama's stepmother did not want him to become king, for she hoped her own son would be king instead.

To get rid of Rama, she tricked the young prince's father into sending him away to the forest.

So Rama and Sita went to live there, in a tiny cottage.

Life was peaceful, until the day that Sita was spotted by the demon king, Ravana.

Ravana had twenty arms and ten heads. He had eyes as red as the brightest fire, and teeth as sharp as daggers.

"A beautiful princess!" he hissed. "I shall make her my wife!"

Chapter Two

The next day, as Rama and Sita were out fetching water, they saw a deer.

"Could you catch it for me?" Sita asked her husband. "I would like to keep it as a pet."

But the deer was a trick, sent by the wicked demon.

For as soon as Rama had gone deeper into the forest, chasing it, Ravana swooped down on Sita. He swept her up and away, over the treetops.

Sita was terrified, but she knew that she must leave a trail for her husband to follow.

So she pulled off her golden anklet and threw it to the ground below her.

Then she tossed down her earrings, one after the other. And lastly she removed her shiny scarf.

Below her in a tree, a little white monkey looked up and saw her jewels falling.

"The stars are falling from the sky!" he thought.

Chapter Three

At last Rama caught up with the magical deer.

But as soon as he touched it, the animal changed into a demon and took off into the air.

"It was all a trick!" cried the prince.

He rushed back to the cottage, but his beautiful wife was nowhere to be seen.

"The demons have taken Sita!" he moaned. "If it is the last thing I do in this life, I shall find her!"

He started to look for her. Deeper and deeper he went, into the very heart of the forest, until at last he saw something sparkle in the leaves.

"Sita's golden anklet!" he cried.

"An earring!" he gasped, a moment later. "And another!"

A little further on he caught sight of something bright, fluttering in the trees.

"Sita's scarf!" he exclaimed. "The one I gave her on the day we were married!"

Chapter Four

Suddenly, there before him was the little white monkey.

He was Hanuman, the monkey king. He led Rama to a great cave, under a hill.

Hanuman had sent word to all the monkeys in the world that they must gather there.

"The demon, Ravana, has stolen Sita!" cried Hanuman. "Rama and his wife are friends to the animals. We must find her!"

So the monkeys went off in every direction. They searched the forest, the mountain and the plain.

At last, Hanuman's group came to the edge of the land.

There, far out to sea, stood an island, and as soon as the monkey king saw it, he knew that Sita was there.

Chapter Five

The island was surrounded by massive rocks and stormy seas, and the other monkeys could see no way to get ashore.

But Hanuman was the son of the wind god. He climbed to the top of a hill, sucked in the wind all around him, then leapt out over the crashing waves.

The monkey king landed on the island and soon found Sita, near the palace of the evil demon.

"No!" he heard her cry. "I will not marry you, Ravana! It is Rama alone that I love!"

When Sita saw Hanuman, she knew straight away why he had come.

"Catch!" she cried, tossing him a pearl from her hair. "Take this to my husband, to show him that I am still alive!"

Rama was overjoyed at the news.

Hanuman called all the monkeys to gather at the shore, but the waves were growing even bigger, and they could see no way to get across.

"Build a bridge!" ordered the monkey king.

So they gathered rocks and grass, sand and soil.

They mixed them all together and built a giant bridge, all the way from the shore to the island.

Then they marched across, and the terrible battle with the demons began.

Chapter Six

"I have come to rescue my wife!" shouted Rama, when at last he made it through to the palace.

"You will have to kill me first!" cried the demon king.

With a mighty swing of his sword, Rama sliced off one of his heads. But, to his horror, another one grew in its place!

Again and again Rama chopped, and again and again Ravana's heads reappeared.

His sword could do nothing. So Rama raised his bow.

The gods of fire and wind guided the arrow and, in a burst of flame, it pierced Ravana's chest, killing him stone dead.

Rama went to find Sita, locked away in the depths of the palace.

They hugged each other warmly, then came out and called a halt to the battle.

After thanking Hanuman and the monkeys, Rama and Sita returned to their own country to rule as king and queen.

The gods threw flowers from the sky, the people lined the streets with flags, and in every house an oil lamp was put in the window to welcome them home.

They ruled, happily and well, for many years, until it was time for them to leave this life on earth and return to heaven.

And that is the story of Rama and Sita.

It shows us how goodness and truth can win over evil, as one little oil lamp can brighten the darkest of nights.

And every year, at the festival of Diwali, Hindu people light small oil lamps, or divas, inside their homes, to remember.